POODLESTAN

POODLESTAN

A Poodle's Eye View of History

by BÊTE NOIRE

as told to PAUL-MARC HENRY

ILLUSTRATED BY PETER USTINOV

REYNAL & CO.   NEW YORK 1965

Foreword

It is with very real pleasure that I take up my pen upon the invitation of my old friend, and indeed occasional enemy, Bête Noire; can a friend be true if the frontier of enmity be far away?

By now it must be abundantly clear to other poodles, other dogs in fact, and even to some men, that I am an English poodle. Naturally, like English men, we have been submitted to the influence of France, and I have known poodles boast of their Norman blood, but strangely enough never when there was a French poodle present. The Gallic strain has given us our quick reactions, our ability to jump to conclusions and through hoops, our moments of hysteria, but in our case these qualities are tempered by an indefinable Englishness—our predilection for being out in the rain, and for leaping straight from puddle to sofa without any of the painful red-tape which usually lies between adventure and comfort.

We also boast that exquisite period of liberal self-examination before we bring ourselves to bark at an intruder. Our eyes move upward to a neutral surface in order to place all our sensory capacities in the service of our ears. We habitually hold back our bark, because like our English owners, we are continually haunted by the nightmarish possibility of having to apologize in case of error. This tendency has developed into a complex over the centuries, so that like our masters, we frequently apologize without having committed any fault, just to be on the safe side. Apologies to us are like bones put away against a rainy day in the Bank of the Spirit.

However, we are animated by a national sense which is no less belligerent for being prudent. "We don't want to bite, but by jingo, if we do . . ." is our animating force. A contributory element in our slowness to rise to an occasion is our desire to give the burglar a sporting chance before we raise the alarm. For the benefit of foreign dogs I feel I ought to define the term "sporting chance." It means lessening your advantage to a pitch where your victory is never in doubt, but where it will seem the more meritorious owing to its narrowness. A very British invention, and no other nation assesses its sporting chances with such sickening accuracy. German shepherds, for example, are notoriously clumsy about this, and make fools of themselves very often. Does any other dog have to stoop to the shameless propaganda of Rin-Tin-Tin in order to protect its public image?

I notice that I set out to speak about Bête Noire, but that with the ingrained modesty of my race I have spoken mostly of myself, or rather, of ourselves. Well, what is there to say about Bête Noire? She is French, of course, with all that that entails. A high intelligence pressed into the service of frivolous small-talk, an immediate and somewhat thoughtless bark, a petulant rather than a dangerous bite, an uncertain and sometimes desperate way, and yet, one can't help liking her. A "grande dame," especially when pregnant.

Her book suffers nothing in translation. Each sniff, each slobber has been given its full value, and I recommend it heartily for beasts and owners of all ages. Historically there is little to quarrel with, except that our contribution to victory and defeat at Agincourt, Crecy, Waterloo and Tenchebrai has been somewhat ignored, which proves that if we have learned anything from man, it is prejudice.

TOPHILL CHUCKLES OF STONYBRIDGE (Lord)
As dictated to Peter Ustinov

The Kennels
Stonybridge Park
Shipbourne
Tonbridge

A Momentous Question: Whither Poodlestan?

My morning walk from 51st Street to Central Park is usually made in small laps punctuated by hundreds of stops and brief encounters. There, I, Bête Noire, a black Miniature poodle of French origin, actually born and bred in Paris, meet brothers and sisters of every conceivable size, shape, color, and manner of dress.

One day the omnipresence of our race in the midst of the wealthiest city in the world suddenly struck me. Here at the height of his power, with the greatest accumulation of wealth per square yard in history, man is living as a slave to four-legged creatures and four-wheeled machines. He is squeezed by both—out of his space by the car, out of his peace by the poodle.

How and why is it that poodles have climbed all the way from the cave to the penthouse, from rags to riches, from underdog to uppercrust? Between two fireplugs I paused, thunderstruck by this momentous question. Could the rising power of Poodledom be channelled into a new and glorious nation, Poodlestan? A nation spanning East and West, and finding in its past the seeds of a new and brilliant future?

To find out meant I had to consult more than five hundred volumes in various languages where the factual evidence of our past greatness as revealed by human beings lies scattered and unrelated. I had to give up siestas, bone chewing and vague contemplation and discover how much the human race is indebted to Poodlestan from the origin of time to the opening of outer space.

It soon became clear to me that the man-poodle relationship is one of the keys to the understanding of world evolution.

In the sea of time man and poodle are obviously in the same boat. We are told repeatedly that over-crowding leads to disaster. At the present time, the human population of the world has reached the amazing mark of three billion. One hundred and ninety million human beings in the United States alone have to cope with twenty-five million dogs and—horror of horrors!—thirty million cats. True enough, American Poodledom as yet counts officially a modest million subjects, but its incredible rate of increase gives rise to the greatest hopes—or fears, of course, depending on which way you look at it.

Every day three hundred pure-bred puppies apply for official registration, one every five minutes. Assuming this poodle pet population explosion goes on unchecked, it will outstrip the human one by the year 1984 in the United States alone. The available evidence makes it reasonable to predict that we poodles will easily be on the crest of the demographic wave.

Worse still—or better—many of us could not care less whether poodles are miniatures, toys, or standards; whether they are registered or not, or whether they pay their club dues. It is, therefore, a normal assumption that each registered poodle puppy stands for at least two pedigree-shy, carefree tax evaders—which means two million avowed or hidden citizens of Poodlestan openly or secretly longing for national recognition.

We have moved a long way indeed from the scattered tribes of poodles who lived in the land beyond the Rhine, where our nation is said to find its origins. We can be proud of our tall, black, curly-haired ancestors who showed their mettle by keeping up with the fierce Germanic tribesmen in their westward movement out of the depths of Asia to the wild forests of Europe.

To take a larger view Poodledom is but a part of dogdom in its general evolution. Initially man needs dog. Now, however, in these days of affluence, dog needs man. As we know only too well, the human brain is unable to perform without leisure.

At the dawn of civilization the shepherd dog, herding and guarding the first domesticated animals, guaranteed some of that leisure to the human breed. Without a dog, man would have spent his time running after sheep and cattle rather than meditating on the laws of nature. Without dog as his faithful hunting companion and courageous fighter, man would have long since vanished from the earth's surface, a natural victim of the ravenous appetite of beasts of prey. In a word, without Dog the shepherd, Dog the hunter, Dog the pet, human civilization simply could not even have gotten off the ground.

With a dim premonition of the shape of things to come, the ancient Egyptians placed the dog, very naturally, at the apex of an imaginary hierarchy of gods. It is true that

Anubis, the dog-god of the Egyptians, was not a poodle; on the other hand poodles have no desire to be gods. We dislike human and canine sacrifices; we condemn obscure rites. Tempting though some may find it to speak of divine origins, it is, rather, to an exceptional combination of gifts that the rising power of Poodledom can be traced within the general ascent of dogdom. From the very beginning of time our race seems to have inherited a special gift of pinpointing the right type of association with the right people at the right time and the right place. All writers agree on one point: the intelligence of us poodles is "scarcely less than human." We naturally find this statement rather condescending, but if we discount human egocentrism we can accept it as our due. Anatomists acknowledge our remarkably developed frontal sinuses as indicating the intellectual class we belong to. Modern genetics recognizes our contribution to the strengthening of the blood lines of other German, French, Italian, and English dogs. Yet in this mixing of strains we have managed to keep our own poodle identity.

As a French patriot I have naturally been interested in our early migration to France. Let us remember that around the fourth century the land of the Gauls, occupied and civilized by the Romans, had become an easy prey for the warlike Germans. France itself derives its name from the Frankish clansmen who brought with them their martial customs and their women, and were escorted by their poodles. The invaders found hunting dogs, shepherds, and even warrior dogs, such as the powerful race from Brittany who fought so well in the games of the Roman circus. It is likely that German poodles, for their part, found the local bitches quite attractive. They have, indeed, a certain charm. Soon a smaller and more rustic version of our breed spread across the land—the Barbet, which became the people's poodle.

His native intelligence and his democratic instincts made him the affectionate pet of Jacques Bonhomme, the prototype of the stolid French peasant who survived centuries of man-made catastrophes to emerge, with his Barbet-poodle, as the real victor of modern revolutions.

Thus, firmly grounded in an earthy and vigorous ancestry, I am ready to accept as kissing kin the miniature Maltese whose blood may flow in the veins of our toy brothers. The Latin and Greek poets extolled their refined and sensitive beauty. The beautiful Issa, portrayed on the lap of a Roman governor, who adored her, is the first of a long line of toy poodles that progressively infiltrated the higher ranks of society.

Finally it is worth recording that our race, born in the east, has moved steadily westward along the arduous paths of invasion or the mysterious roads of trade, to settle finally in its most recent and prosperous environment: the United States. This demonstrates that, throughout time, poodles have shown a marked preference for civilizations where man can firmly assert his hold on nature and, clearly, the poodle his hold on man.

In the sixties, and in the most affluent of human societies, the animal world—led by poodles—has now triumphed. From the lowly status of producer of cheap power, rewarded by kicks and whip lashes, horses and dogs have moved to the lofty position of consumers courted on every side for what seems to be their new potential.

Part One

I Look Back at History

O Vires Illustribis
Cave Canem!

I

Before we describe our newly won state of affluence let us glance back at world history. Let us remember that inequality between the poodles who manage by a shrewd marriage to find a niche in good society and the unlucky ones who remain sons and daughters of the people must not grow too wide. In 1789, just before the blood bath of the French Revolution, poodles, lapdogs, Maltese, and other Miniatures were feted, petted and pampered. On the lower strata of society the anonymous Barbets were working acrobats, dancers, musicians, and cart-pullers, keeping company with the much abused farmer and artisan.

While Barbets hunted duck, dug for truffles, and turned the spit for their masters, perfumed bitches, queens of this cruel and daring world, gamboled in the gardens of palaces. Such inequality could not endure. One fateful day of October 1789, the starving men and women of Paris, escorted by their dogs, walked all the way to Versailles to demand that the King and Queen of France rejoin them in the city where neither brioches nor bread could be found.

Thisbe, the lap dog of Marie-Antoinette, Queen of France, became then and there one of these charming and faithful witnesses of a bygone age marked by passion and cool detachment. Thisbe, perfumed and beribboned, was present when affairs of state were discussed between the good-hearted Louis XVI and his charming blonde, blue-eyed child-wife. She was also on hand when the dashing Chevalier de Fersen made love to his royal mistress with all due dash.

Thisbe drank milk every day and ate cake while her lowly cousins had to go without bread and submit to the scalpel of the vivisectionists. She played in the gardens of the Trianon and the park of Versailles without risking any contact with stray sans-culotte mongrels. When the King and Queen with the little Dauphin were forced to go back to the angry and starving capital of Paris, Thisbe had to leave this closed-off paradise. The days spent playing hide-and-seek behind statues and well-shorn bushes or bathing in the Piece d'eau des Suisses were over. Thisbe wandered instead through the dreary, cold corridors of the Tuilleries Palace surrounded by jeering crowds and barking Barbets. A worse fate was to be expected: secret messengers came and went. Long, tearful evenings were spent with Marie-Antoinette and the Dauphin; sadness was shared, and tenderness mutually provided.

Then the frightening trip to Varennes with everyone in disguise; Thisbe especially was hidden carefully, since only aristocratic dogs travelled poste-haste in those days. Finally the parting.

The Queen was taken with her children to the forbidding jail, the Conciergerie, where Thisbe was refused admission by the brutal guards.

Had it not been for Arnaud, the dressmaker, Thisbe would have starved waiting for Marie-Antoinette at the prison gates. It is said that Louis XVII, the unfortunate Dauphin, as well as his mother, asked in vain to have Thisbe share their long hours of captivity. One day the desperate poodle took her own life, jumping from a high window into the River Seine. With her passed the era of the pampered few.

II

I feel a certain nostalgia for this period. What nascent Poodlestan lacked in numbers it made up for in exclusiveness. In another troubled century, another ill-starred King of France, Henry III, lavished huge sums of money on lap Poodles. According to historians he took scores of us wherever he travelled with a whole retinue of attendants. He carried his favorites in a basket slung round his neck. This, plus the company he kept with gambling, fighting, swearing, and dancing long-haired *mignons*, hardly improved his public image in an age of fanaticism and bigotry.

Worse still, he was suspected of practising witchcraft and flirting with the devil. While I see in the young King

—with poodle hindsight—a liberal bent on restoring tol-
erance between warring factions, his narrow-minded contemporaries abhorred his equivocal attitude in love, life,
and politics.

In that dangerous age pets had to be able to sniff enemies
of the state and would-be murderers from a distance,
and keep their muzzles shut when a crime was committed
for kingly reasons. In August 1589 Liline, Titi, and Mimi,
the King's preferred Miniatures, were in attendance when
the young Dominican friar, Jacques Clement, was admit-
ted to the inner chambers of the royal palace of St. Cloud
to petition the king. They immediately smelt danger;
barking angrily, they warned their master. It was too late.
Already the monk had drawn from his sleeve a short knife,
the width of two fingers, and thrust it into the King's
abdomen a paw's breadth below the navel. The King died
of his wounds a day later, a victim of an age that took
politics and religion seriously but failed to heed the warning of poodles.

Two years before Mary, Queen of Scots, another victim
of this blood-thirsty era, had paid with her head for being
on the wrong side of the channel.

Up to the last minute of her long confinement in the
dark castle of Fotheringhay the unfortunate Queen cherished the image of the sweet and sunny Loire Valley. As
the young bride of Francis II she moved with the court
from château to château in the great and joyful cortege of
royal masters. Horses pranced, dogs frolicked. No doubt
many solitary evenings were spent by Mary Stuart talking
to her favorite lap-poodle about its ancestral land. Her

faithful confidant stayed with her in the execution chamber, hidden in the folds of her vast skirts. When the foul deed was committed, the fear-stricken witnesses saw the pet poodle, covered with royal blood, clinging to the beheaded body of its beloved Queen.

III

Nobody seems to know what happened to Mary Stuart's dog. We are at liberty to imagine that one of the good servants took care of the bereaved puppy and that the proud line of Scotland and France somehow survived side by side with the dour Scotties.

During the following two centuries pretty poodle faces began appearing in paintings of aristocrats, their mansions, families, and gardens. We had a hard time, however, competing with the toy Spaniels, close relatives of ours—with a touch of oriental blood, I'm afraid—which Charles II of England had brought into eminence. Spaniel dynasties became established at a time when Poodlestan was still groping for its own autonomy and identity. From the court to the salons the Spaniel craze spread quickly. In the eighteenth century a great man of letters, Horace Walpole, crossed the channel to court the clever Madame du Deffand and, as a token of fidelity, brought back to Strawberry Hill, her favored Spaniel, Tonton, a well-known toy Spaniel. After the death of his mistress, Tonton succeeded

in taking the place of Walpole's cherished pets, Tory, Pata-
pan, and Rosette.

A century before, in France, the Marquise de Sévigné
and the ever-young Ninon de Lenclos had helped to
launch the pro-Spaniel fashion. It took the lovely Countess
de Sabran, a great believer in the life of nature (who found
solace in exotic birds and flowers sent to her by the Chevalier de Boufflers from the faraway islet of Gorée off
Senegal,) to restore the miniature silver poodle as a trusted
messenger of love. Her poodle became her confidant, ready
to understand and sympathize with Eleonora's grief at the
Chevalier's absences.

But the eclipse of the Spaniels was about to come. As
soon as the blood bath of the French Revolution was over,
England witnessed a strong comeback of our breed.

A dashing French aristocrat, Count Alfred d'Orsay, became the lion of an English society extremely fond of
French manners, provided they were those of the *émigrés,*
not those of the uncouth Napoleonic soldiers. No wonder
that in such a moral climate the *émigré* dogs and their
offspring, like their masters, learned nothing and forgot
nothing. The "dazzling ephebus" Alfred d'Orsay, prome-
naded proudly with a beautiful white Standard whose
posture and demeanour were so imposing that Edwin
Landseer, a member of the British Royal Academy, portrayed him in one of the best-known paintings of the nineteenth century, called "Laying Down the Law".

In a prospectus describing the engraving from this
celebrated picture I find the following statement:

It may be interesting to those Philosophers who like to trace effects to their causes, to know the origin of this composition. A French poodle, the property of Count D'Orsay, was resting on a table in the attitude represented by the Artist, when it was remarked by a certain noble and learned Lord who was present, and who, from having held the Seals, was certainly a competent Judge, that "the animal would make a capital Lord Chancellor." On this hint, which seemed palatable to the Artist, he set to work; and the result was the admirable Picture, now in the possession of the Duke of Devonshire. The Portrait of one of His Grace's canine favorites has been added to the original group, and appears in the Print—the little Spaniel immediately over the high-bred Greyhound, who looks askance, with such a significant expression, at his plebeian neighbour the Bulldog.

The following Verses, suggested by the Picture, are from the pen of Thomas Hood, Esq., the Editor of 'The New Monthly Magazine:'—

LAYING DOWN THE LAW

. . . I am Sir Oracle,
And when I ope my lips let no dog bark.—*Merchant of Venice.*

If thou wert born a Dog, remain so; but if thou wert born a Man, resume thy former shape.—*Arabian Nights.*

A Poodle, Judge-like, with emphatic paw,
Dogmatically laying down the law,—
    A batch of canine Counsel round the table,
Keen-eyed, and sharp of nose, and long of Jaw,
    At sight, at scent, at giving tongue right able:—
        O Edwin Landseer, Esquire, and R.A.,
        Thou great Pictorial Esop, say
What is the moral of this painted fable?

To me, the moral of this painted fable is that dogdom at long last came into the open, and that the lordly, dapper, aristocratic poodle knew exactly what he was doing when he caught the attention of a certain "noble and learned Lord".

IV

If the *émigré* poodles landed on top in the country of
Wellington, their plebeian Barbet cousins were having a
hard time in the land of Bonaparte. We shall see presently
the eminent role they played in the vainglorious Napoleonic campaigns. After the Battle of Waterloo there was no
mercy for those who shared the triumphs of their com-
rades-in-arms; they were reduced to begging for food and
shelter. For many an *ancien combatant* there seemed to
be nothing left but to die or return to carnival life, so long
the mainstay of poodle identity.

In a manifesto published in the French papers by the
Poodles of France and Algeria in the year 1844—four
years, I note, before the Communist Manifesto by Marx
and Engels—I found the following eloquent appeal: "We
have spent a lifetime in acquiring one thousand and one
agreeable talents, all to the advantage of man: we turn the
spit, we carry our master's dinner in little straw baskets,
we guard his treasures, and we defend them better than
any lock and key, including those of Mr. Fichet (the
French inventor of the safe), we dive into icy rivers to
rescue children who have seen fit to risk drowning on the
pretext of amusement, and lastly, we play dominoes; we
even dance the Polka".

Far from being a mere protest against a threatened increase of the pet tax in the city of Paris, this revolutionary

LAYING DOWN THE LAW AFTER EDWIN LANDSEER

document opened daring vistas on the not-too-distant future of triumphant Poodlestan. The names of the authors have been recorded in poodle history: Azor, Trim, Rox, Diane, Bob, and Betty. In addition, more than three hundred thousand petitioners, mostly poodles, also scratched their signatures.

They denounced the conceited and narrow-minded approach of the Western European powers to the problem of animal welfare and turned to the East for inspiration. In Isphahan, the beautiful Persian city of a thousand domes, a hospital for dogs had been functioning since the sixteenth century. They recommended that in Paris, and in each provincial city, taxes on pets should be earmarked to create similar institutions that would take care of the wounded, abandoned, invalided, and retired poodles, as well as other breeds.

Following the fashion of the times, poodle prophets envisioned a Golden Age when all men would be brothers and animals cousins; then a great banquet would be held —vegetarian, of course—and a toast raised to the memory of the bipeds who defended the rights of their four-legged relatives and acknowledged their just claims.

The Paris Manifesto has, in fact, been implemented. Dog money is being used for dogs. In addition, sizeable sums are now redistributed between the human sector of the economy to the animal sector. Yet, the banquet has not taken place. Perhaps we are still not quite ready for it. Perhaps we are not such vegetarians after all.

V

Dandies and Manifestos were not enough to persuade the world to reconcile itself to the rising power of Poodlestan. Aristocrats and Proletariat wanted to be amused, not exhorted. The useful functions performed by dogs were in due course to be taken over by mechanical slaves. Nobody would dream nowadays of asking a poodle to turn the spit when electricity can do it better and possibly cheaper. So far, however, no robot can dance the polka, walk the tightrope, or sing Mozart. This we have done, and will go on doing, except that now it is for our own pleasure, not to make a living.

Poodles made their entry on the stage early in the eighteenth century. The well-known poodle couple, Marquis de Guillerdain and Demoiselle Poncette, danced the minuet to the delight of Queen Anne. Their names are quoted to this day as proof of our excellence in the performing arts. The creators of the modern circus, Dobney, Sampson, and Astley, in London, and Nicolet in Paris, put in the ring horses and dogs who followed the trail blazed by the Petit Marquis and his mistress, Poncette.

Individual prodigies managed to emerge in their own right, such as Munito, nicknamed the Canine Newton. His Italian master took him round the theatres and salons of Europe. He performed for the benefit of street urchins and factory workers as well as for earls and princes. He

UNITO, THE NEWTON OF THE CANINES, EXPLAINING
n ADVANCED THEORY TO ITALIAN MEN OF SCIENCE

could play dominoes and chess, count, read, and write. This black poodle travelled with a well-educated goat. After the performance their master had to hire a carriage for both. Munito sat proudly near the driver, barking grandly.

Munito had many imitators, genuine or fake. One of them was advertised in Paris as "the scientific bitch". Curious passersby were invited to "honour with their presence a poodle who can read and count with the aid of topographic maps and can answer queries from the audience on Ovid's *Metamorphoses*, geography, Roman history, etc." She could count the number of persons in an assembly, and write down all words. She could demonstrate the four basic rules of arithmetic, tell time, and describe colors.

Were Munito and his followers charlatans or prodigies? The same question has arisen in so many other cases about so many other performers and believers in the supernatural that we are left to ponder.

Franconi and his Italian compatriot, Corvi, followed the great master of Munito. Signor Corvi launched his own Paris theatre with real, four-legged actors, and a few bipeds. In the park of St. Cloud, in 1850, he attracted children with a show described vividly by a contemporary: "Corvi was dressed in black. At a signal, from all corners of the stage poodles, monkeys, and a pretty white goat rushed to the footlights and saluted the public, dancing round and round their director. A table was brought on stage and set by the monkeys. The poodles sat at table waiting for their dinner, which was served by their two-legged friends. However, the wine steward drank from the bottle instead of filling the glasses. It was only when the poodles were well fed that they were ready to work. They skipped rope, singly, in twos, and in threes, as the two monkeys looped the rope faster and faster. Then they waltzed. In keeping with the martial spirit of the times, in came the invalid, limping on three legs, who finished by walking on his two left legs.

"The finale was a concert with violins, flutes, and bugles, as well as tympani. The only music, though, that reached the ears of our youthful spectators came from the cacophony next door where the great king, Cocombo, and the beautiful princess, Manoutapakika, of Polynesia, were eating live rabbits".

In 1860 the poodle Bianca amazed the Italian skeptics with her ability to translate and to write in nineteen languages.

Bianca would climb on a large table, sitting in the centre, the different letters of the alphabet disposed around her. After she was given a word to translate, she would close her eyes and look thoughtful for a brief moment, then pick up the letters one by one, forming the word. Then she gravely sat back and barked to mark the end of the sentence. Human observers agreed that this ability was the result of systematic education and a gift for learning. No one dared make the silly accusation of witchcraft made in similar circumstances by the ignorant Puritans of the seventeenth century.

Let us mention in passing Jojo and Toto, stars of the all-poodle show at the Nouveau Cirque of the Gay Nineties, which the children of Paris enjoyed immensely. Their

"THE INIMITABLE DICK"

most famous act was the rescue of a fortress by red-coated poodle firemen.

"The Inimitable Dick", probably the greatest star of all times, was a black Poodle, three feet high on his hind legs, who was nicknamed the Loye Fuller of the canine world. Presented by the attractive Miss Doré, he achieved the most impressive, astounding effects by using his front legs with sticks, twirling a long black train, or by standing on his front legs with wind blowing through scarves, like an early version of the dance of the seven veils. La Danse Serpentine, La Gavotte Stephanie, La Valse and the Polka held few secrets for this bright student of the "eccentric clowness", Miss Doré, who was herself educated by the great Hachet-Souplet, the Descartes of modern training methods.

Hachet-Souplet tells us in his own words of one of Miss Doré's poodles, marvelously obedient, who would follow the smallest twinkle of the eye and who could balance on a horizontal stick, holding in its mouth a rolling ball, and also a juggler's frame loaded with twirling plates and glasses. Using a racket, he could toss a ball in the air while a fellow-poodle waltzed on his front legs, balancing a lighted lamp on his head.

"The Inimitable Dick" number was usually followed by the display of brute strength of a poodle, Hercules. Endowed with such a strong jaw that he could carry enormous weights, he also fired a cannon with a big bang; finally he carried a ladder that a smaller poodle climbed up.

There seems to be no limit to what poodles might do in

this century of progressive education. Rols from Darmstadt was taught to tell true notes from false during family
musical performances. Together with his owner, Herr
Friedrich Schwartz, he became one of the most feared
critics at the opera house. A single muted bark from this
stern listener could send singers or flautists back to their
metronomes.

Another German poodle, Rolla sang the *Lorelei* with
her partner, the Reverend Treiber. Mr. Habeneck, the
director of the Paris Opera, educated his poodle associate
to sing in chorus with other poodles magnificent pieces by
Mozart.

It is recognized by contemporaries that the imitative
impulse in dogs—and more particularly in poodles—is
very strong, and "that there is no reason why it should not
extend to the imitation of articulate and musical notes so
far as the structure of the vocal organs render their repro-
duction possible".

This musical gift is abundantly exploited in the circus
world. Poodle orchestras play for the public to this day.
That there is a certain decay in this ability shown in so
many well-documented cases by our ancestors of the last
century is apparent in the contemporary emotional barking, heard nowadays on jukeboxes.

The circus, for better or for worse, has been for more
than one hundred and fifty years our stepping-stone to
fame. Children have been our strongest supporters.
Through their sons and daughters, nephews and nieces,
adults are progressively brought into our orbit.

No less of a personage than the Count of Toulouse-

ROLS VON DARMSTADT
POODLE MAESTRO

Lautrec found in the poodle world of the circus "a special brand of humanity, a humanity that is not going to the dogs". As an aristocrat looking for color and life in what even then threatened to become a dull, bourgeois world, he went with his friend, Tristan Bernard, to the great circus Fernando—the successor of Franconi—to admire an amazing troupe of performing white poodles.

Toulouse-Lautrec made friends with the clowns, Chocolat, Footit, and Bole. Poodle actors jumped on his lap. He patted the horses' well-polished mahogany rumps. He painted them all, with us poodles shown dancing or smoking a pipe.

Circus is now Big Business. The public wants bigger and better acts, with larger and wilder animals. Still, no performance is complete without horses, poodles, and clowns, as well as beautiful bareback riders.

VI

With such a record nobody can, or for that matter does question the place of Poodlestan in the performing arts. That place is first place.

It is true that quite a few dispute our claim to martial glory. In a learned dissertation on the military dogs in the French Army, written seventy years ago, I find the poodle eliminated as a potential combatant because "although he is extremely intelligent, he is not sufficiently gifted in the five senses, especially in the sense of smell, which is enough to prevent his becoming an excellent dog of war".

This obviously comes from a basic misunderstanding. It may be true that poodles were not in the first ranks of the dog-fighting squadrons which, since the time of the Greeks and the Romans and throughout the European wars, inspired terror in the enemy. I have seen pictures of these armoured brutes, with metal collars and blood-thirsty looks; most of them are of giant size, specially bred for war at the expense of any other abilities.

Similarly, no poodles worthy of note have ever been selected to act as tracking dogs pursuing Indians at the time of the Conquistadores or retrieving escaping slaves at the time of the infamous trade. The modern and distasteful duties performed by the big Police Dogs are most unattractive to us.

On the other paw, when fighting calls for intelligence, fidelity, and last-ditch resistance, history shows the poodle in the front lines. All amateurs of poodle biography know the strange and glorious story of Boye, the big white Standard of Prince Rupert, a nephew of King Charles I of England.

Boye was given by his Britannic Majesty's Ambassador in Vienna to Prince Rupert when he was taken prisoner after an unsuccessful campaign in the Low Countries. Of pure Danube blood, Boye was of a breed now very scarce; it has been described as having "the eyes large and almond-shaped, genuine black diamonds; the nose, shiny anthracite black; the coat, bursting with whiteness; the

POINT TROP N'EN FAUT!

DARK THREATS
OF WAR
AGAINST ENGLAND

size of a Newfoundland dog; a majestic mane; the legs, thin and nervous; well-palmed feet; a face as intelligent as it is good; daring as a lion, strong as a bull, a lamb-like disposition, and the ability to swim and dive like a seal."

It is said that the powerful Ottoman Sultan uttered dark threats of war against England unless he was given a puppy from this Danubian sire.

Prince Rupert went back to England where he was appointed the King's General of the Horse by Charles I who, in 1642, decided to fight against the Puritans led by Cromwell. Like Satan, Boye could speak many languages; he would prophesy future events through the medium of his master's footman. Everywhere Rupert went he took Boye with him; Boye immediately became the target of the fanatic Roundheads' hatred. They suggested that Boye was once a woman under a profane metamorphosis. In other words the faithful companion of Rupert was branded with the sign of the witch. Angry pamphlets were written with imaginary dialogues between Boye and more commonplace canines. Fanatics went as far as to call upon the assistance of the recently established Puritan colonies of New Egland who had a special knowledge of how to order about these dog-witches.

Boye appeared to be as efficient in the council chambers as he was fearless on the battle field. Even Royalists were reduced to shame in their indecisive deliberations by his begging and barking tricks. Puritans swore that he could swallow cannon balls under fire and appear like a white ghost behind their lines. He was called "protector of

his master, confounder of the King's enemies." There was
no doubt but that by his sole presence he put a hex on
them. Boye died gloriously on the battlefield of Marston
Moors on July 2, 1644; this marked the decisive reversal of
fortunes for Charles I.

The triumphant Cromwellians demanded that witches,
sorcerers, the Pope, and the devil himself be invited to
mourn at the funeral of Boye. Prince Rupert, now deso-
lated and unsuccessful, tried to forget his heroic companion by many daring adventures, including an ill-fated expedition to the wild coasts of Guinea; he mourned Boye
for fourscore years before dying.

VII

Many of our ancestors who had shared the joys and sor-
rows, the poverty and the gaiety of the people of France,
gave their lives for their country. Answering the call to
arms in the Revolutionary Wars many dogs walked from
Marseilles to Paris with the battalions that, after repulsing
the German invasion from beyond the Rhine, gave to
France its inspiring national anthem.

At that time recruitment was done on an informal basis.
After the population had been assembled in the main
square of the village to the roll of drums, an officer in a
blue uniform asked the able-bodied men to volunteer,
offering them no reward but honor or a glorious death.

Grandfathers, fathers, and sons came forward to join the colors, leaving behind the strong women to care for the land and wait for them, trembling and proud.

Many of us, as members of the family, also left everything behind, including the coziness of the humble hearth where happy evenings had been spent with the good smells of thick peasant soup.

It was collective heroism. Triumphs and failures, victory and defeat. The historian, unable to quote every feat of these indomitable people and poodles, could focus on but a few, such as Moustache, the contented poodle of a grocer. He marched all the way from Caen to Italy, trotting proudly along with a regiment of Grenadier Guards, climbing the icy pass of the Alps, and finally leaving behind father-proud puppies in Milan.

Moustache is said to have seen action from Marengo to Austerlitz. He sacrificed his crisp curls for the stark military cut. He could recognize the smells and sounds of the enemy, and bark accordingly; he could also tell the French from the Austrian drums. We see Moustache at Austerlitz, surrounded by the enemy but fighting to save the colors covering a dead French ensign. We see him tearing off a piece of the standard and trying to bring it back to camp.

After an enemy bullet broke one of his legs, he was found two hours later, half-dead, but with his jaws clenched on the Tricolor. He was mentioned as a hero in an imperial order of the day, signed by Marshall Lannes, which now entitled him to a tricolor collar with a silver medal, on one side of which the following words were en-

graved: "Moustache, a French dog, a brave fighter entitled to respect". On the other side: "At the Battle of
Austerlitz, he had his leg broken while saving the flag of
his regiment". Moustache was presented to the Emperor
Napoleon, for whom he performed various tricks, including his most famous one, lifting his leg at the mention of
the Emperor's enemies.

Men and dogs of this period walked. Going from
France to Italy to Spain or, for that matter, all the way to
Russia, meant going on foot, marching night and day.
During the bivouacking, the military poodles performed
for the soldiers and shared their coarse meals. They
wagged their tails when the men looked happy and told
stories; they kept them warm at night in the icy Sierras of
Spain and on the windswept steppes of Russia. They
swam across the glacial waters of the Berezina when
thousands of men and horses, fleeing the sword of the
Cossacks, fell from broken bridges.

The legendary dog, Moustache, died in Badajoz, Spain,
in a rear-guard action when the sun was already setting on
the brightest hours of Napoleonic history. As a bitter after-
math, the French like to add that Moustache's grave was
violated by the Inquisition, and his bones burned in a
grim ceremony reminiscent of the bygone ages of witchcraft.

Another hero, Sancho, knew a better fate. The Marquess
of Worcester found the faithful fighter exhausted and
starving, lying on the grave of his master after the bloody
battle of Salamanca. Sancho was immortalized in a portrait
painted of Charlotte of Wales, one of his great admirers.

MOUSTACHE ON THE FIELD OF AUSTERLITZ

The faithful Moffino, whose companion-in-arms, an Italian corporal, was thought lost during the crossing of the Berezina River, trotted all the way from Russia to Italy to find him. Alone, bedraggled, and starving when he reached Milan, he was barely recognized by the Corporal. At the mention of his name, Moffino found just enough strength to bark happily and wag his tail. We can assume that Moffino and his master lived happily ever after.

Moustache, Sancho, Moffino, and many others, are but names for the Unknown Poodle who in so many guises participated in the wonderful epic of the Napoleonic era. As one of our human friends, the Count of Ségur (who also walked all the way from Moscow to Paris during the fateful year of 1812) says, "It seemed as if the great convulsion (of the French Revolution) had been nothing more than the labor pains of the birth of one man. He commanded the Revolution as if he were the genius of that terrible element. At his voice, it came under subjection. Ashamed of its excesses, admiring itself in him and attaching itself to his glory, the Revolution ignited all Europe under his rule".

Years later in solitary exile, on the rock of St. Helena, Napoleon made a curious remark. He said that a poodle had made him stop the massacre of Austrian prisoners and wounded after a fierce battle. Was it that the deep and penetrating look of a dying poodle, covering the body of his dead master made him realize the identity of fate linking our two races in the face of final negation?

This was echoed a few years later by Victor Hugo, a poodle-lover and an admirer of the great Corsican, who asked, "Whither the Man? Wherefore the dog?"

VIII

Napoleon had a high regard for the military virtues of our race, but on a more personal level he had reason to be less enthusiastic. His first wife, the beautiful Josephine, had made the mistake of leading a gay life and parading an inglorious, but attractive, lover, Lieutenant Charles, in Paris when the young Bonaparte, long-haired and ill-kempt, was routing Austrians in Italy and the Mamelukes in Egypt.

Her lap dog Fortuné, a cuddly miniature of the poodle race, was, just like the unfortunate Thisbe, a silent witness to his mistress's escapades. Fortuné had also been involved in the bloody days of the Terror. As the wife of a good Republican officer, de Beauharnais, who was considered too soft with the Royalists and had to pay with his head for his moderation, Josephine was thrown into Robespierre's prison. Fortuné managed to carry messages concealed under his collar from Josephine's children, Hortense and Eugène de Beauharnais who survived to take their part in the extraordinary Napoleonic adventure. Madame Mère, the stern Letitia Bonaparte, took an instant dislike to the discreet puppy companion who refused to testify against Josephine.

Five years later the Emperor was to be shattered by the fact that yet another poodle took part in one of the most fateful decisions of Napoleon's career, the killing of the Duke of Enghien.

VICTOR HUGO : WHITHER THE MAN? WHEREFORE THE DOG?
THE DOG   : WHITHER THE DOG? WHEREFORE VICTOR HUGO?

Talleyrand branded this cold-blooded murder as worse than a crime: it was a blunder. The Duke was a victim of a love affair that took him across the French border from the safe exile of Germany once too often. He used to go escorted by his poodle. Both were taken to jail and transported in great secrecy by the French *gendarmerie* to the dreary fortress of Vincennes. Napoleon, who saw himself surrounded by Royalist assassins, wanted to strike a swift blow at the ever-present conspiracy and show that he would not hesitate to shed the blood of royalty for the salvation of the Revolution. The innocent Duke of Enghien, a direct descendant of the great Condé who fought at the same time as Prince Rupert, was shot at dawn without judgment or warning. His poodle refused to leave him until the last moment. He had to be taken away forcibly from the shallow grave of his master. Many tears were shed by Josephine and Hortense over this unfortunate event in which Napoleon showed so much cold-blooded determination and a poodle so much devotion. I must confess that the Duke's poodle was not as resentful in the long run as the Royalists. Adopted by the commander of the fortress, he became a good Bonapartist. After the poodle's death, his new master had him stuffed and put under a glass globe as a paragon of faithfulness.

IX

What a strange century the sixteenth must have been! The animal world was burdened in all directions with the sins and failures of the human one. The goat was said to bear a strong resemblance to various demons and to smell as much as they do. The elusive cat was the familiar guise of lesser spirits. Black dogs took on supernatural sizes and shapes. The thin frontier between the domesticated and the wild was criss-crossed by mysterious beasts terrorizing superstition-ridden peasants.

In a word, the established human order was threatened by bitches in the shape of witches. It reacted with ferocity.

In England and Scotland witches were burnt with their dogs, like Mother Bennett and Suckin, Agnes Sampson and Elva. Protestant and Catholic were at one in this European sport. It is not merely a coincidence that the middle of the sixteenth century, as far as we know, was positively crowded with females of talent. Mary Tudor, Marie of Guise, Queen Elizabeth of England, Mary Queen of Scots (whose tragic fate we already know), Marguerite of Parma, Marguerite of Navarre, and all the *Gallantes Dames* described by Brantôme, were enough to give an inferiority complex to any male in any century. The result, among others, of this topsy-turvy influence is to be found in the fat kings and bluebeards who killed as many women as they married, and praying mantis', like Catherine of Medici, who saw so many of their sons die prematurely and their daughters-in-law lose their heads.

We have recognized a victim of fanaticism in Boye, a valiant poodle defender of seventeenth-century Poodlestan in the making. It took another hundred years before England could philosophize about witchcraft and all but completely forget about it. It shocked me to discover that Germany, the ancestral land of Poodlestan, also needed another century to emerge, and then just barely, from superstition and witch-burning.

X

Our philosophical and literary journey from the age of darkness to the centuries of light started appropriately from Provence and Tuscany, lands of clear fields and green gardens.

Superior minds sought in isolation from human beings and the company of dogs the necessary freedom for creative work. In 1346 Petrarch, in his enchanting retreat of Vaucluse, sang the praise of "de vita solitaria," which could not be complete without the best companion of a meaningful and deliberate solitude. We are told that Cardinal Colonna, knowing Petrarch's love for dogs, gave him a white puppy of Spanish origin. Was it a poodle? On the basis of internal evidence, most probably.

"Continually he gives amusement . . . with his shrilly bark he imitates the children when they sing . . ." Only poodles can sing.

Some years later, another brilliant Italian, turning away from a world he could explain but not transform, Machiavelli took a poodle with him to his little country house near Florence to compose in peace a treatise of practical politics which has been the thinking poodle's basket-side book ever since. In addition our brighter ancestors were associated with the daring minds who risked their security in the endless quest for truth. Poodles consorted with sorcerers, witches, and envoys of evil powers.

Monsieur, a black poodle, kept company with one of the wizards of the sixteenth century, Cornelius Agrippa, no less than a private counselor of Charles V, Emperor of the Holy Roman Empire. Later accused of being an incarnation of the devil, Monsieur committed suicide after the death of his associate by drowning himself in the River Saône, near Lyons, in France.

Cornelius Agrippa believed that the Great Architect (God) communicates the virtue of his omniscience through the animals, as well as through the angels, the heavens, the stars, the elements, the plants, the metals, and the stones.

Cornelius had many followers among his contemporaries, such as Paracelsus of Zurich, Nostradamus of Provence and Georg Sabel of the Rhineland who called himself Dr. Johannes Faustus. The most innocent of their animal companions was apt to be branded with the curse of witchcraft. When Faustus, during his years of wandering,

MACHIAVELLI'S
COMPANION

stopped at the College of Bâle, he was accompanied by a black dog with long curly hair. His colleagues were rightly surprised when the mysterious poodle took the form of a servant and brought Faustus food. The distinguished vagabond was nicknamed the "European beachcomber of the sixteenth century". Legend and superstition soon picked up this strange figure. The man found dead in a tavern at Württemberg in the 1540's with his head twisted and his face bearing a sardonic smile became the symbol of a generation that tried to get from the devil a quick short-circuit to truth. His black dog became a diabolic faker who could change at will to brown, white, or red, light up his eyes with flames and, indeed, take fantastic forms. A synthetic devil, Mephistopheles, a product of minds obsessed became our alter-ego. Two centuries later Goethe could sniff out the "enchanter's cunning" in a poodle's most innocent trick. Adding insult to injury he saw in the poodle "no trace of mind, but drill alone." No wonder Goethe's Dr. Faustus had nightmares when his black dog, after snarling, howling, and barking, took on abnormal proportions, becoming "an hippopotamus with fiery eyes and teeth terrible to see". Could this have meant that Goethe's philosophy of light was playing hide-and-seek with the powers of darkness? To a thinking poodle this is a major puzzle.

XI

At last another great German philosopher decided to live with poodles alone. It took Arthur Schopenhauer to bring the world a better understanding of the intricacies of man-poodle relationship. Credited by his biographers with glimpses of insight into the mystery of the unseen and helped by the constant company he kept with the most intelligent and silent of beings, the poodle, Schopenhauer turned solitude and obscurity into sources of peace and happiness. He learned from the sacred texts of India and the constant company of poodles the equal dignity and holiness of all animated existence. Animals are an integral part of a total creation of which mankind is a mere participant. Man may live on a more comfortable level of existence, yet his own life is but one form of the "will to being," the root of the universe.

In the extinction of all desires lies the path of happiness. A carefully guarded mediocrity of material circumstances, a regular schedule of life, revolving around well-established habits and escape from the malice of men, lead to this fundamental purpose. In our "world of masquerade", friendship with four-leggged creatures became a natural antidote to the falsehood and trickery of two-legged ones. Schopenhauer chose to look into the honest faces of his poodles rather than into the beguiling eyes of a woman.

TWO CENTURIES LATER GOETHE EMBODIES THE EVIL
SPIRIT IN A BLACK POODLE

For those interested in his recipe for semi-detached living, here is a perfect sample of a Schopenhauer day.

No human companionship of any kind, except, *à la rigueur*, a cleaning-woman. An organized concentration with the over-riding purpose of understanding the meaning of life. A small furnished flat with neighbours unseen and unheard. A poodle. A stroll every morning at the same hour with this poodle. (First with his snow-white bitch, Atma; second with his brown dog, Butz.)

After a morning stroll in the leafy suburbs of a nineteenth-century German town, back to the study, and three hours of writing. The sharing of a Spartan lunch with the (by then) starving poodle. A bit of a rest, then two more hours of work, then another promenade. On his way back to town, the philospher allowed himself a stop at his club to read the London Times and drink a stein of beer. Sometimes a concert or a lecture after a brief supper—with his poodle tucked away in bed. Then to sleep.

This went on every day for more than twenty years. In this timeless existence, poodles became the personified present. They enabled this true philosopher to appreciate the value of every unburdened hour.

Intellectual communion between man and poodle had thus reached a peak. Some malcontents were bound to react. Friedrich Nietzche spread the rumor that Schopenhauer had in effect "a poodle brain". The philosopher of the superman had no room for the superdog even though he himself, of course, finished in the dog-house.

Before I describe how animals have finally been accepted as masters by mankind, I feel I must pause and express my deep gratitude to the lonely bachelor of Frankfort who, contrary to his compatriot, Goethe, found compassion and wisdom in our angelic company rather than the devil incarnate.

XII

That Schopenhauer struck a very sensitive chord was proved by the lively reaction of the anthropological philosophers. He was considered an arch-villain. Frightful consequences were predicted for a society that could be so obsessed by the huge mass of sensitive misery in the world, and make it the principal object of its attention. Convinced partisans of white supremacy predicted that the Western world would soon be reduced to the level of the Eastern lands where Buddhism has nothing more to offer than a passive Nirvana in which man has to be content with a life of total peace and fraternity with beasts included in both creation and re-incarnation. Scorn and rage were poured on the protagonists of animal rights.

I find all this very puzzling. Why wouldn't the world agree that creation and evolution embrace man and beast alike?

The fact seems to be that metaphysics do not agree with Poodledom or Animaldom at large. Accused by religious fanatics of representing one more incarnation of the devil, animals were also rejected by such apostles of reason

SCHOPENHAUER SHARES HIS SPARTAN
LUNCH WITH HIS COMPANION

as Descartes, who accused them of having no soul. Their body was only a machine to be dissected, alive if possible, to demonstrate whatever is automatic in the functioning of an animal's body.

Descartes and his followers, seeing the machine in both man and beast, wanted to draw a frontier between those two. Man thinks, therefore he is, said Descartes. The dog reacts, he thought, but does not feel or think. The preacher, Malebranche, a contemporary of Louis XIV of France, felt justified in kicking his pregnant bitch, since "she could not feel anything". To many a disciple of the brilliant Blaise Pascal, the cries of a dying animal were no more than the creak of the turning spit. The end of the seventeenth century saw Italian doctors of great European reputation, such as Columbo, Redi, and Nassari, turn their backs on St. Francis of Assisi, cutting live animals into pieces for the sake of a non-existent science. The air-pump became the favorite instrument of torture for learned ladies and gentlemen of France, Italy, and England, who indulged in sociable vivisection parties. The Invisible College of the Philosophers of Oxford patronized blood transfusions, experimental drowning, and slow poisoning, all inflicted on defenseless creatures under the false pretext of science. It took great names during the eighteenth century, such as the Earl of Shaftsbury, Jeremy Bentham, and Alexander Pope in England alone, to condemn the delight taken by so many in the torture and pain of other creatures as "wholly and absolutely unnatural as it is horrid and miserable".

At the turn of the nineteenth century, animals, workers

and paupers were still thrown into the same despised batch by European aristocracy then in top form. The English, in particular, drank and hunted heartily. The populace took pleasure in cruel games. The rights of animals were trampled underfoot. While the rich man's dog followed his master and helped him in his cruel expedition, the poor man's dog drew carts, competing cheaply with mules and horses. In between, the enlightened middle class seemed to care only for the comfort of its own pets; it was apt to look with distrust on any intrusion by the government in the natural law of the free market under the guise of the protection of the weak.

Seldom involved in either sports or hard labor, poodles danced their way into the gilded cage of mummery. They could not, however, remain insensitive to the pitiful stories of their fellow-canines dragging carts full of rags and bottles from the garbage heaps of the rich to the shanty towns of the poor. They did not remain deaf to the cries of mongrels slaving at treadmills. They did not ignore the abominable trade of the dog-catchers, who got blood money for gathering innocent tramps into the death holes of many a brutal city.

Let's recall that it took more than ten years for the British Parliament to make legal the daring ideas of Lord Erskine and Richard Martin and pass the first legislation in the Western world recognizing the rights of animals. The 22nd of July 1822, date of the foundation of The Royal Society for the Prevention of Cruelty to Animals, was but the first milestone on a long road. A road ambushed by enemies and skeptics in England as well as in France and the United States.

NIETZSCHE DEPRESSED BY THE IDEA OF THE SUPERDOG

On the afternoon of 3 July 1850 General Delmas de Grammont faced, on behalf of the Government of the Second French Republic, an assembly determined to poke fun at this converted military officer who was unwilling to kill a fly. The great name of Chateaubriand was thrown into the debate on the side of proposed legislation for the protection of animals, but it did not stop the catcalls and dog-barks of the derisive legislators. The good general may have been unfortunate in some of his examples of man's cruelty to animals. The grandsons of the spectators of public executions where human beings were drawn and quartered or beheaded in the Place de la Concorde a few decades before could hardly take seriously the antics of Emperors Domitian and Nero who used merely to cut rabbits up alive.

The legislation was passed, immortalizing the name of the then obscure General Grammont. French national pride was challenged by his words: "Wherever animals are dealt with gently, they are gay, cheerful and enjoy man's company. In Germany and England horses are not beaten or insulted and they turn out to be more docile and sensitive. It seems that of all people the French are the most inhuman. Perhaps they inherit the natural ferocity of the Gaulois, hardly concealed beneath our silk stockings and ties".

Anyway, the French National Assembly could hardly expect to be compared unfavorably with the Mother of Parliaments on the other side of the Channel.

In the United States ridicule was also poured on the head of the great Henry Bergh, who a decade later, tried to awaken the Americans to the rightful claims of animal suffering. The wealthy and aristocratic New Yorker went out in the open, standing night and day in the streets of the adolescent metropolis, pulsating with animal life.

Horses pulled heavy streetcars; cows produced adulterated milk; dogs were set to fight dogs; rats and cats were skinned alive. Cockfights drew delighted audiences. Enterprising Spaniards thought of bringing the bloody excitement of the bull ring to the thriving, dirty and stimulating metropolis of the 1860's.

After many fights with many a brutal coachman and an impatient and derisive public, Henry Bergh managed to have approved by the Senate and Assembly of the State of New York the charter creating the American Society for the Prevention of Cruelty to Animals on the 10th of April 1866.

As in England, the Society had to fight on a broad front. Cruelty to dogs was then less obvious than cruelty to horses. Odd companions-in-suffering were thrown into this universal crusade, which left no heart of stone unturned. Even sea-turtles got pillows under their heads after their long voyages before their final jump into the soup.

It was high time for mankind to protect animals. In fact, human science was just discovering that man was, after all, but a part of a larger animal world. Charles Darwin stated: "He who is not content to look like a savage at the phenomena cannot any longer believe that man is the work of a separate act of creation. He will be forced to admit that the close resemblance of the embryo of man to that, for instance, OF A DOG (the emphasis is

DARWIN
ILLUSTRATING
A
POINT

mine) the construction of a skull, limbs, and whole frame on the same plan with that of other mammals . . . and a crown of analogous facts, all point in the plainest manner to the conclusion that man is the co-descendant with other mammals of a common progenitor".

No wonder that humans reacted most strongly against the demolishing of their cherished delusion of an anthropomorphic, anthropocentric world. For some curious reason they lay the blame on the monkey, comparing in the process Darwin to one of them, perhaps because monkeys look so much like men. A distinguished British Prime Minister-to-be, Disraeli, asked himself the famous question: "What is the question now placed before society with a glib assurance that is most astounding? The question is this: 'Is man an ape or an angel?' We know the glib reply: 'My lord, I am on the side of the angels.' "

I submit that Disraeli would not have objected so strenuously had the question had been, "Is man a poodle or an angel?"

Before Darwin or after Darwin, the modern world in the making was inspired, in its love and understanding of animals, more by love, charity and pity than by biological identification. Schopenhauer and the average poodle-lover were ultimately more interested in our brains and heart than in our skulls and limbs.

When the R.S.P.C.A. held its international jubilee meeting on 22 June 1874, the Cause seemed triumphant. The Duke and Duchess of Edinburgh and the indefatigable Lady Burdett Cowtts ("a staunch advocate of the practical education of all classes in the absolute duty of man

towards the lower animals"), the Earl of Harrowby, the
Bishop of Gloucester and Bristol and more than a hundred delegates from foreign and British societies gathered
in the newly-constructed wonder of the age: The Royal
Albert Hall. More than four hundred prize-holders, aged
eight to twenty, received rewards for essays written in
favor of animals.

In this field, as in many others, the Victorian world
basked in an orgy of self-congratulation.

Science and benevolence, for human beings and animals alike, appeared to be reconciled. What science itself
had the means of inflicting in the way of wounds, the
spirit of benevolence could heal by pouring on oil and
wine. In other words, Grammont, Henry Bergh, and Lady
Burdett Cowtts found themselves in happy communion
for the elimination of cruelty to two- and four-legged
creatures with Mr. Dunant, the creator of the Red Cross.

XIII

Such a display of man's acceptance of the growing power
of animals provoked furious reactions Right and Left.
Indulgence and compassion were criticized for opposite
reasons. On the Right, the march to progress was alleged to
be paralyzed by too much attention paid to weakness,
misery, or biological failure. The neo-Darwinians talked

KARL MARX
1818-1883

about the survival of the fittest as a good thing. On the Left, the stark realities of the class struggle could not fit into an Oriental ideology which professes a belief in some eternal cycle of life and death.

Already Marx and Engels, unimpressed by the Paris Poodle Manifesto of 1844, denounced in their own Manifesto the members of the R.S.P.C.A. as representatives of "this part of the Bourgeoisie which is desirous of redressing social grievance in order to secure the continuous existence of the conditions of the working class, organizers of charity, temperance fanatics, hole-and-corner reformers".

Marx, curiously enough, was a compatriot of Schopenhauer. He failed to see the secret thread of our own progress as a class within the classes. Had he known better he could indeed have detected in our own ranks some class struggle. Too often Barbet poodles were seen in the streets, growling at well-coiffed pets; bitches of the upper classes were rejected from their own world because of an unfortunate encounter. Marx's colleague, Engels, also showed a blind spot when he maintained that "labor is the source of all wealth". Poodles know that all wealth is not due to labor, and certainly all labor does not lead to wealth. As for the two vehicles of man's superiority over the rest of the living world, "the hand and speech," we know that, without either, Poodlestan has proven it possible to "dominate the dominators and exploit the exploiters".

By the end of the "imbecile century," animals had become the center of a raging controversy between metaphysicians, psychologists, paleontologists, social scientists, and politicians.

Man, in fact, was on the defensive. Having had to accept the continuity of "the nervous process of man and animal", so clearly demonstrated by the great Russian physiologist, Pavlov, he had to prove that there still existed between the two a tremendous "qualitative" difference. In this Pavlov was not far from Descartes and Malebranche, except that he did not deny that dogs, like men, could suffer. Events of human history were soon to prove that the poor dogs reacting to the bell of the Russian doctor were no worse—or better—off than men rushing to slaughter to the call of martial music and the bellowings of dictators.

XIV

Naturally man began to wonder whether or not he was the master of his own fate, a fate carrying him to endless material achievements and increased spiritual solitude.

Another great dog-lover, Maurice Maeterlinck, devoted his life to answering these questions. He believed that man is in fundamental agreement with the universe. There is a secret unexpressed understanding between man and creation. Everything is pre-arranged. Mysterious correspondences exist between places, animals, and men. Life is a continuous process that permeates the whole

AETERLINCK BELIEVED THERE WERE MYSTERIOUS
RRESPONDENCES BETWEEN PLACES, ANIMALS AND MEN

chain of living beings from the bees, the white ants, the spiders, the dogs, the flowers, and man.

Man, knowing man, knows he is "absolutely alone on this chance planet; amid all the forms of life that surrounds us not one, excepting the dog, has made an alliance with us."

Maeterlinck turned out to be, contrary to his philosophical predecessors, a complete flop in animal-man relationships. Out of eight dog companions, at least two committed suicide. A third died prematurely of a fatal illness.

His sister tells us the depressing story of his poodle, Adhemar, *"the misunderstood"*:

The poet and the visionary, who by flashes of intuition was able to grasp the continuity of the evolution process culminating in the consciousness of consciousness, had no patience with the unfortunate Adhemar, who is described by his master as "crazy, incoherent and unsettled". Instead of measuring the whims of Adhemar against the background of a far crazier and more unsettled human world, Maeterlinck sent the unfortunate pet to the country and left him to board with strangers, whereupon the misunderstood poodle starved himself to death.

A great fuss is made nowadays of the author of *Pelleas and Mélisande* and *The Blue Bird*. Yet the vague and dreamy romanticism of the misty philosopher does not hold water. Between Atma, the world soul, and Adhemar, the misunderstood, between Schopenhauer and Maeterlinck, there is an unbridgeable gap of unrequited love.

XV

After World War I, in which so many animals and men perished, long-limbed women wanted long-limbed companions with pin-heads and pointed noses. In post-war society, dogs were supposed to be fashionable and not very intelligent. For more than twenty years Greyhounds, Alsatians, Smooth and Wire Fox Terriers, and trembling Chihuahuas stole the show. Wealthy dog-owners were apt to use their pets as status symbols rather than muses. We poodles know from experience what this means to our breed. In fact, the 1920's, just like the 1720's, witnessed an eclispe in the popularity of Poodlestan, a forced retreat to meditation, in preparedness for the glorious age to come.

Chronicles deliberately forgot our past deeds and glory. Our substantial contribution in the scientific field was ridiculed by authoritative magazines such as *Vanity Fair*. Facetious editors, failing to see that the great Albert Einstein would, in the last analysis, offer the key to the physical destruction of the universe and not to its construction, compared the father of relativity with one of us: "This pleasant, mild, and wind-blown poodle/ Has less than nothing in his noodle/ 'Twixt him and Mr. Albert E./ There is thus no relativity."

The poodles of the 'twenties had as much in their noodles as their illustrious ancestors, *Vanity Fair* or no *Vanity Fair*. The ranks of the novelists were progressively

POODLESTAN UNABLE TO KEEP UP
WITH HISPANO-SUIZAS AND
GREYHOUNDS
DURING THE BARKING TWENTIES

infiltrated, as had been those of the philosophers a few
decades back. In France alone the list of brilliant writers
by poodles possessed ranges from Crebillon the elder (an
obscure tragedian) through Victor Hugo and Edmond
Rostand to contemporary writers. Maurice Dekobra, who
made a fortune pouring out racy novels in which beautiful
spies crossed Central Europe in sleeping cars at the then
stupendous speed of fifty miles an hour, was also a chron-
icler of *La vie très Parisienne*. His poodle called Picrate
(immortalized by the good Dr. Mery) displayed in the
complicated game of the love-triangle the same uncanny
gifts as Munito did in the field of pure mathematics.

This child of the new century could recognize which
pair of slippers to bring to the right lover at the right time
without betraying his warm-hearted mistress, a dancer of
the Folies Bergères.

Picrate may very well have met Rag, a handsome grey
Standard, who around the same time owned Francis
Carco, the delightful poet of Montmartre. Every morning
Rag went to fetch the morning *croissants* at the bakery
next door, where he ran into debt by buying on credit, and
devouring at once, what he regarded as his normal per-
centage of the sale. He strolled in every street of old
Montmartre with its welcoming corners, little bistros, and
terraced gardens, soon to be demolished and lost to time
like the world of Toulouse-Lautrec, Nini Peau de Chien,
Valentin the boneless, Jesus La Caille, and the melancholy
ghosts of *la belle epoque*.

Picrate and Rag were the contemporaries of Basket I,

the celebrated poodle of the neo-Parisian, Gertrude Stein, and her friend, Alice B. Toklas. Gertrude Stein was picked up by the white poodle puppy in the last years of the 'twenties. "He had blue eyes, he had pink eyes, a pink nose, and white hair." He jumped into Gertrude Stein's arms. Alice B. named him Basket "because I had said he should carry a basket of flowers in his mouth. Which he never did."

In being picked up by a poodle and in liking Picasso Gertrude Stein was totally consistent. She made a point of following an anti-fashion that somehow became *the* fashion. Nobody really cared about Juan Gris when she decided to write his life story. Hemingway was just another young man about Paris when she encouraged him. She was the first to see in Scott Fitzgerald "the only one of the younger writers who writes naturally in sentences".

Basket shared in her discoveries. A romantic painter, Francis Rose, had the luck to exhibit his work near the pet shop where Basket I was regularly bathed and groomed. Rose became a familiar of the house and a well-known artist.

A few years later another white poodle, Basket II, kept company with Gertrude Stein and Alice B. Toklas during their exile in the years of World War II in the south of France.

In the Americas the uphill fight for recognition of Poodlestan had barely started, but some prominent figures in the literary world such as Alexander Woolcott proclaimed admiration for a race whose origins antedate the Mayflower by many centuries. Woolcott's own poodles, Gamin and Harpo, "clearly regard themselves as having a special relation to the human species". Woolcott erred in tracing this bond "to the fact that for a thousand years their forebears travelled with the French circuses and in all that time had no point in their lives except a person, no home at all save the foot of the boss's bed wherever it might be". We historians of Poodlestan know better.

XVI

When Rufus I, closely followed by Rufus II, took over the powerful British Empire through the emotions of Sir Winston Churchill, the veil of secrecy that for so long concealed our rise to power was torn asunder. Whereas Boye had to fight his way through the Court and finally suffer death on the battlefield in order to make an imprint on English history, Rufus was present at every meeting between the Chiefs of State who were thought to be deciding the fate of the world.

Sir Winston received a Nobel Prize for his literary accomplishments; so did John Steinbeck, in revealing circumstances. To our minds, the masterpiece of this prolific writer is a rambling chronicle of a trip taken jointly by Charley, a Standard poodle, and his legally-owned master. It describes an America sinking slowly into total boredom and barely rescued by emerging Poodlestan. Where Schopenhauer was humble enough to recognize that poodles were the personified present, Steinbeck, who is not a philosopher but who accepts evidence, concedes "that in some areas Charley is more intelligent than I am". On the other hand, Charley is said to be "abysmally ignorant. He can't read, can't drive a car, and has no grasp of mathematics". (Munito must have turned in his grave.) It is more likely that Charley was never given a chance to manifest gifts other than "the slow imperial smelling over the annointing of an area".

To Disraeli's rhetorical question as to whether man is on the side of the apes or the angels, Steinbeck adds another one: "Of course, his (Charley's) horizons are limited, but how wide are mine?"

When the learned gentlemen of Stockholm chose Jean-Paul Sartre as another worthy recipient of this famed Prize, they must have been aware of the invisible bond which connects irrevocably such widely different, but equally formidable, human personalities.

The philosopher of existentialism is said to have found his roots in Heidegger and Kirkegaard. Stockholm guessed better. Hector Malo, a laureate of the French Academy, is in fact more important in the making of this great mind unafraid of rendering unto Poodlestan its due. The truth, as revealed by Sartre himself, is that he knew *"Sans Famille,"* the *chef d'oeuvre* of Hector Malo, "by heart," and that when he had turned the last page, he knew how to read. This at the important and formative age of five.

Sans Famille is the epic of an imaginary poodle, Capi, who was a perfect interpreter of the romantic, rather lachrymose nineteenth-century. Capi was a performing poodle. He could salute like a veteran (Oh, ghost of

Moustache). He could find his master, Vitalis, in the wine-scented lanes of Paris and the gin-smelling alleys of London, and finally save his foundling friend, Remi, from legacy-conscious villains. No wonder Sartre was impressed for the rest of his life by this book which opens with Capi sleeping arm-in-arm with Remi after the little boy had been sold for forty francs to a vagabond musician and circus operator.

No wonder that the great philosopher-writer states boldly in the memoirs of his childhood: "So I am a promising poodle."

But how on earth did the Gentlemen of Stockholm find out?

Part Two

Is Poodlestan
An Affluent Society?

O Tempora
O Mores!

I

Charley, receiving the Nobel Prize for literature through Steinbeck and Capi through Sartre a few years after Rufus was crowned for his immortal achievements through Winston Churchill, marked the climax of our fight for human recognition. The time has now surely come to take stock.

Three million poodles are scattered all over the globe with the greatest concentration of population in the wealthiest part of the so-called overdeveloped countries. Our race holds a firm grip on the wealthiest individuals. All this without in any way having abandoned a solid and age-old footing in the older lands of Western Europe where our ancestors have been patronizing great minds for centuries. For all intents and purposes Poodlestan and Western civilization are one.

For us dogs modern society is ready to provide, in addition to food, such products and services as: clothing, jewelry, grooming, studding, judging, advertising, car and air transport. Conservative estimates put the target of our dog-food consumption at one billion dollars a year in the United States alone. This figure of potential American consumption sets the pattern for poodle-developing countries in other parts of the world.

I ran across the following statement by Walter B. Armstrong of Standard Brands:

"In the past ten years dog food dollar volume has grown at a rate again as fast as that of margarine and at a rate about equal to that of cold cereals".

According to Armstrong, "Despite this dramatic growth, the dog food industry still is in its infancy relative to the potential that exists today". He estimates that "less than one-third of all food fed to dogs today is commercially prepared so that even though the industry has grown fantastically, the surface for potential is no more than scratched".

I, a French poodle, shudder at the thought that makes Mr. Armstrong's mouth water. His two-thirds of "unscratched potential" represents what remains of the solid tradition of home-made cooking, which is fighting a losing battle against the can-makers and can-openers. It also means that *de facto*, if not *de jure*, the family dog is not excluded from the family table and reduced to a solitary bite at regular intervals in the corner of the kitchen. This consumer's resistance is the subject of grave preoccupations by the market analysts. In a recent article in *Printer's Ink* the problem is thus stated: "Pet owners' resistance to prepared pet foods is the main stumbling block to further growth of one of the biggest small-item markets in this country. But larger ad budgets, broader campaigns, greater use of media are breaking down this resistance".

The problem seems to be further complicated by the fact that, according to the learned article, "It is not enough that a pet be enthusiastic about a prepared food. The marketing of the product must be based on the owner's acceptance. Because of their *emotional involvement* with their pets (the emphasis is mine) research shows pet owners believe their animals should have a diet comparable to a human one and offering almost as much variety". No details are given on how this "research" was actually carried out. By questionnaire, by direct observation, by sample survey, with an adequate use of electronic computers? How many dogs did actually disagree with their masters, notwithstanding their "emotional involvement," we are left to ponder.

The fact remains that legally, at least, no dogs are allowed to do their own shopping. Discriminatory legislation bars them from supermarkets and butcher shops. I would suggest, therefore, to the distinguished members of the Pet Food Institute that until food equality before the law is guaranteed to human beings and dogs alike, the hard sell will end in a soft flop.

To be sure, dog owners are trying to bridge the gap between Madison Avenue and Poodlestan. In a recent study on the acceptability of meatballs in gravy for suburban dogs, eighty-seven per cent were ready to state that their dogs "ate eagerly", while eighty per cent would go as far as to report that the interviewed puppy "liked the food better than the present brand he had been eating".

This does not mean much because many other relevant factors are missing, such as the degree of compulsion to which the unhappy consumer was submitted by systematic starvation, deprivation of choice bits from his master's plate, such as roast chicken, calf's liver *Veneziana*, veal sweetbreads with cream and mushrooms, and so on.

The question is to know whose resistance the promoters are trying to soften. I am afraid that labels emphasizing indulgence like "Something Special for Fido", or "Cat a picky eater? Try these tabby tempters", as suggested in the *Progressive Grocer* in 1961, will not do for intelligent poodles. The Association of National Advertisers had to take note of some market research by the "center for the study of audience reactions" indicating "that consumer irritation over commercials could be a severe block to receptivity". Let it be a warning to those who believe that intelligent and well-educated members of our breed will gobble pre-cooked, nondescript meat just because an abstract Fido with a low IQ, market-analysed by hucksters, is expected to like it.

II

Food is not everything. Poodlestan is bound to be affected in more ways than one by the free interplay of market forces that it has little or no control over. Even our love-life is in danger of being organized by outside agents who pretend to monopolize biological decisions affecting our breed, supposedly for our own sake but, in fact, for money.

Many ordinary female poodles are deprived of the natural joys of motherhood. The reproductive act is put at a premium with stud fees skyrocketing. A campaign is being waged to license dogs in the same way as pedigreed bulls forcing many into an unnatural celibacy. The threat of artificial insemination and sperm banks looms large on the horizon of over-fed, over-dressed and under-sexed citizens of Poodlestan.

By a strange twist of logic the adepts of the super-poodle doctrine of eugenics beg those who have the interest of the breed at heart *not* to bring to the world any new puppies from their pet bitch unless the proper certificates have been granted. Some go so far as to recommend the culling of undesirable litters.

At the other extreme the enthusiastic supporters of a dynamic biological control are banking on the popularity of our breed to make a fast buck while there is still time. They are ready to put on the market any puppy at any price to anyone. It is rumored that poodles are being sold wholesale, and will soon be found through the super-market chains of this thriving, pet-loving nation. The neo-Malthusians accuse these mass-producers of evading the payment of stud fees and of being ready to let nature follow its course on street corners, drive-ins, and even the back seats of cars, provided the interested partners look even remotely like poodles.

The average price of a six-month puppy can thus be

reduced by more than half, bringing poodle ownership within the range of the vast number of human beings whose annual income remains obstinately within the four-figure bracket. Socially, this may be good and contribute toward making Poodlestan a worthy contributor to mass civilization. Economically it may be ruinous. Those, in particular who want to produce smaller and better poodles tending towards "The Perfect Poodle" make agonizing protests by arguing on the basis of the fundamental "Stud Law" which, I believe, is

$$P \text{ equals } S$$

in which P means market price of puppy and S minimum price of stud fee. The net profit of the breeder can thus be expressed as follows:

$$\text{Net Profit} = (P \times F) - S$$

F being the average fecundity of the average bitch which, unfortunately, remains low. As was said recently by a distinguished breeder: "Poodles don't produce THAT many puppies". On the other hand, one can reduce S!

Be that as it may, population control is the obvious problem of the sixties. The question remains control by whom and for whom.

III

To any well-informed and objective observer, and to a poodle himself, a Poodle is a Poodle. But not to the professional maniac of classification. Over fifteen inches the poodle is a Standard. Under this arbitrary line he becomes a Miniature. Five inches less he is a Toy. The various sizes are affected by the human attempt at biological control.

The Standards somehow remain virtually immune from experiments tampering with their basic physical characteristics. The main reason being that they, and only they can satisfy simultaneously the craving of human beings for stamina and outdoor life, including hunting (only in extreme cases) *and* the feminine longing for primping, clipping, brushing, fussing, petting, and one-way talk. In other words, the Standard remains the nearest approximation to the convertible car; it can satisfy the longings for both sport and status.

The Miniatures and Toys are, unfortunately, embroiled in the Min-Toy controversy which rages on the vast North American continent from the Atlantic to the Pacific, dividing families and estranging friends who would normally agree in their love for Poodlestan. The origin of this crisis can be traced to the beginning of the pedigree craze of the first half of the twentieth century. By creating and making a separate class for registration of poodles under eleven inches (or is it ten?), the world sowed the bitter

seeds of internal strife. Can Miniatures be accepted as pro-
genitors of Toys? A school of thought pointing out the
dangers of recessive genes maintains that males or females
of the Toy size with one Miniature parent are the worst
possible studs or dams, the large size being in effect insur-
mountable unless small Toy genes are brought in to the
point of saturation. Another couldn't care less. The only
way to satisfy everybody would obviously be to create a
new category where recessive genes could be allowed free
play, sitting happily astride the ten-(or is it eleven?) inch
fatal borderline. The name for this in-between, go-
between class, Toy-Min, is a seemingly Far Eastern term
of doubtful origin.

As another factor of division of the poodle world that
threatens its ascendance over the human breed, the question of color has become abnormally important. Being
myself a black Miniature, I may not be quite objective in
this delicate field. I am bound to report that, since the
beginning of our history, three basic patterns—and three
only—are recognizable in the distinguished poodles who
became famous: black, brown, and white. Only in recent
years have the brown been made into café-au-lait, cream,
and pale cream; the white into platinum silver, silver,
grey, and blue. The trouble with black, as one can imagine, is that it has to be diluted. The sixties appears to have
a strong taste for a dilution of brown called "apricot". A
controversial specimen is the parti-coloured poodle. Some
authorities, such as Count Alexis Pulaski, see in this har-
lequin of canines a genuine descendant of the original
poodle.

I am ready to accept the full weight of his authority on the matter. I have no doubt that he disposes of well-documented evidence to prove the point he made in a recent bulletin of the ASPCA, according to which the poodle at the beginning of the seventeenth century was a "black or brown dog with white muzzle and feet; later the mixture became taboo and about seventy-five years ago solid colors became fashionable".

In any case I will give him full marks for protesting the barbarous practice of culling the litters by destroying at birth parti-colour puppies and comparing it "with the insanity such a practice would represent in human breeding if someone decided to destroy all babies born blond or brunette or redhead just because he did not like the color".

In the domain of size and color the temptation of inbreeding is almost irresistible, although it intensifies existing factors without seeming to create anything new. The endless pursuit for fixation by heredity of acquired characteristics and status affects poodles as well as people. The apricot color may call for time, patience, genetic study, mother nature, and imagination as well as sheer love, as suggested by the "Milbrook Poodles". I maintain that a much more hopeful way to improve the breed lies in the use of the electronic computers, which, because of their superior brainpower, are much better placed than anyone else to decide if Marlyn Geisha will like Little Boy of Slade and happily bring together the required genes. We are now informed by the Poodle Institute of Utica, New York, that "the requested desired traits (size, color, char-

acteristics, and championship lines) are placed on an
IBM card and put through an IBM computer. The infor-
mation on these cards is matched with the permanent registered stud data that is stored in the computer. The
computer then selects the stud dogs with the characteristics required". This combination of eugenics and elec-
tronics seems to me irresistible.

Those of us who live hidden in a happy and discreet
home cannot but be extremely disturbed by the merce-
nary exhibitionism that turns the life of a so-called champion into a sordid and frustrating saga. At the height of
our power as a group, psychiatrists note with mounting
apprehension numerous cases of nervousness, timidity,
and even viciousness unheard of in our pioneering days.
Poodle stars are brought to the applause of an ignorant
multitude. Normal pets, craving companionship, are kept
in cages to grow a resplendent fur; they are coached to
walk like Paris mannequins. The brief moment of glory in
the dog-show limelight is obviously no substitute for the
coziness of non-mercenary love. I am told that such
poodles lose pride in their own physique so easily camou-
flaged by padded fur. Fortunately, the lady poodle in
question is not allowed to remove her coat. I shudder to
think of the poor shoulders, bad neck, and inferior pelvis
that would then be disclosed.

IV

I am indeed concerned with the modern trend of poodle over-grooming. Too many unhappy specimens have to appear in public and got involved in the ferocious jungle of beauty contests and show business. The natural look is banned from exhibitions where beauty is but a pretext for hard-headed financial decisions. As Pulaski put it: "Poodle shows have deteriorated into hair-do contests". For instance, the "sans-culotte" clip with a lion's mane in front and completely exposed rear calls for long hours of seclusion in a restricted space wearing hair rollers.

Fortunately, most family pets get a normal hair-cut in professional establishments. The overwhelming majority gambol in "Dutch Town" for winter and in "Town and Country" for summer. We come back from the beauty shop feeling clean and refreshed from nails to teeth to ears. Some family pets manage to get a good hair-cut at home. In isolated communities poodle clip-joints perform almost clandestinely at cut rates, with many a bleeding toe a nicked ear, and razor burn. Innocent puppies kept quiet by strong tranquilizers, return with dazed eyes. Good clipping affects us anyway in the same manner as would a combination of hair-do and mink coak for our mistresses. This is why I do not feel it irrelevant to deal seriously with hair fashion as an important factor in the state of the nation. Let us remember that one single clip, the lion clip, as

practised expertly a century ago on the banks of the River
Seine, coincided with the most vigorous period of Poodlestan in France. (A degenerate Central European aristocracy supported the ridiculous fashion of the "Cordé"
poodle when our forebears had to exhibit overlong greasy
curls.) There was a certain democratic vigor in the happy
period when Barbets and pedigreed dogs could wade happily in the same puddles and be groomed in the open air
by the same handlers.

V

As to fashion and its apparent excesses, I see in it no
threat to the physical and mental integrity of Poodlestan.
Far too much fuss is made over the intemperate display of
showy clothes and boots about town. The latest fash-
ions seem to be no more than the old costume acts that
poodles performed so well through the centuries to amuse
their masters. Poodles can act as geishas, clowns, or film
stars. In so doing they pay a deserved homage to their
wonderful ancestral performers. Children treat us now
with a mixture of respect and skepticism. Adults are more
amused at our antics and act as our best public.

In more ways than one Poodlestan is made a victim of
human snobbery. The Victorians started it all, as they did
so many other things. Poodle registration is a modern disease born in England. The Establishment in the making

ENGLISH
POODLE

ITALIAN
POODLE

wanted to bring law, order, and family trees to those chosen few who participated in its obvious blessings. The first innocent victims of this mania were given plain enough names such as Don, Elmer, Flo, Frank, and Leon.

As can be expected, pushy poodles and good sires from the steppes of Russia and the banks of the Seine forced their way into the ranks of the English aristocracy. In 1874 wealthy Americans named Michelangelo, a black Standard, card holder Number One of what was to become the would-be-exclusive-but-not-quite-so Poodle Club of the U.S.A. The Anglo-Saxon world began weaving a closed network of interbreeding across the Atlantic.

The Germans were not tardy. In 1878, Graffin and Kaiser asked for and got international recognition. Soon the indomitable Bismarck, a heavily moustached champion, based his claim for total domination on the Teutonic origins of our breed. Strange specimens appeared in the first show rings. "Their hair was allowed to grow and was never combed out but continually rolled and twisted with paraffin and vaseline to cause longer and ever-longer cords to be added to the coat".

The excess of this fashion soon brought an adverse reaction. The great Miss Brunker carried the banner for the curlies. England decided that "no dog exhibited by a member as a corded poodle should ever be exhibited as a curly poodle and vice versa. After April 1900, no curly poodle bred from corded parents shall be eligible for the trophies of the Curly Poodle Club." This schism in poodle circles was soon followed by others. Not content with the

black-or-white coloring, poodle breeders introduced to
the world Le Roi Café and Babette Brune as brown inter-
lopers, soon to be followed by blues and apricots. The
great family Whippendale with Mouche, Mouffon Bleu,
Midinette, and Toto firmly planted the apricot line on
both sides of the Channel and of the Atlantic. The Rath-
nally was another of these Mayflower families who com-
peted for honors and, through well-calculated and well-
endowed intermarriage, built up a secure Social Register.

Some individuals were outstanding. The famous Duke
de la Terrasse, familiarly known as "The Duke", was born
of Prince Alexander von Hodelheim and his dam, Leonore
von der Seestadt, themselves bred from the proud lineage
of Prince von Breslingen and Princess Carmen von Len-
nep. To be sure, the Duke, like so many of his kind, became fascinated by the almighty dollar and crossed the
Atlantic to become an American champion.

The stolid Dutch blood line was also a part of the aristo-
Poodlecracy. Jonkeer Baid de Pladjee founded the great
line of Vulcan Champagnes, directly related to the Darcy
and Pommery strains.

On the eve of World War II the Rathnallys, the Piper-
scrofts, the Hockfords, the Nunsoes, the Nymphaeas, and
the Vulcan Champagnes reigned supreme as Brahmins of
Poodlestan. At the lower echelon of Miniature society the
Chieveleys moved from London to Boston to compete
with the Laird of Mannerhead and flourish in the prosperous dynasty of the Firebraves. It is said that one of them,
Firebrave Gaulois, was the outstanding poodle of his
time, a dignified representative of the great tradition of

THE BRAHMINS OF POODLESTAN

the Piperscroft on his father's side and Firebrave on his mother's, Pepita's.

As we know only too well, the tendency of any parvenu society is to subdivide itself in self-perpetuating castes based on systematic inbreeding. The separation between cordé and curlies, in itself no more significant than a change of hair-do, was but a symptom of worse things to come. Behind these imposing names, with family trees almost a century old, lurked the dread disease fatal to many a proud empire: endogamia (marriage within the group).

After the differentiation based on the use, or non-use, of hair oil came the division by size.

As late as 1932, it was still possible in the upper layers of Poodlestan aristocracy for an undersized bitch to fall in love with a tall Standard and have her progeny received in the best salons. A fashionable marriage of the season, for instance, between Mimi of Newlyn's dam (a Standard) and Champion of Chieveley Chopstick (a Miniature) was hailed in the social columns of English Poodle magazines. But in October 1946 a resolution was passed by the Kennel Club of England asking to make poodles and Miniature poodles separate breeds. Any crossing between the two classes from now on must be shown on the birth certificate as a social stigma.

VI

On reflection, I find it disturbing that this process of registration and recorded blood lines (and all that goes with
it) which humans tried to impose on our breed had long
been rejected as an exclusive selection method for human
beings themselves—in fact, since the American and French
revolutions.

I note, for instance, that Basket II, the distinguished
poodle of Gertrude Stein, was saved from starvation during the dark days of the German occupation in Paris in
1940 because, as the holder of a pedigree, he was entitled
to a ration card delivered by the Mairie. At the same time,
the proletariat, the Barbet poodles had to survive on the
Black Market. The fact that this same proletariat, all in
all, did not do too badly seems to me irrelevant. Coming
back to Paris from the well-protected seclusion of the
Lyonnais Province, Basket II saw, with his mistress, many
dogs "lots of them, such big dogs too, and not so very
young". The many convulsions of Paris, such as the Great
Revolution and the smaller ones, and the siege by the
Prussian army in the winter of 1870-71, saw the starving
Parisians eating everything including cats, rats, horses,
camels, and elephants—but never dogs.

In other words, discriminatory legislation in favor of
"thoroughbred dogs" was not even necessary. As Gertrude

PRUSSIAN
POODLE

Stein put it, "Well, one way and another way you did keep your dog, sometimes the restaurant gave you left-overs or the butcher or if your dog was a great favorite in the street you put out a basket and people put in scraps; one way or another you did go on keeping your dog."

So much for class distinctions.

Conclusion

I would suggest to the advocates of a stronger Atlantic Community a study of the methods and achievements of our nation-in-the-making before embarking on premature schemes. They might discover that our secret lies in the systematic promotion of diversity of color and size within the *same breed*. It is a systematic emphasis on universal rights and equality for the apparent benefit of the animal kingdom, in order to serve, finally, the effective promotion of Poodlestan.

I have travelled enough to know that our domination of a united Western world cannot be the end of our story. The symbolic meaning of the sad fate of Thisbe during the French Revolution is not lost on us. What would be the use of sitting happily with tail wagging on top of a Cadillac-conscious world when unfortunate underdogs have to scavenge for food in the garbage cans of starving humans? Should we put all our eggheads in one basket and refuse to admit the extraordinary achievements of non-poodles in the non-capitalist world? In any case, the descendants of Munito should take a sober view of the fact that ordinary monkeys flown straight from the jungles of Africa were rocketed into space after a brief spell of training at the very same time when the enormous potential brain-power of American Poodlestan was left untapped. Surely what a monkey can do a dog can do better! It took a Socialist country, the Soviet Union, to give the lie to anthropomorphic monkey-conscious capitalist veterinarians.

Why should American scientists fetch from a faraway primitive country a technical expert to assist them in their race for space when they have right at home the accumulated knowledge and wisdom of loyal Poodlestan? It will probably remain a mystery until the damaging evidence is released to the public. The fact is that a non-poodle, Laika, was orbited into space as early as November 1957, whereas the overfed Chimpanzee, Enos, had to wait another four years to make two earth circuits. True Laika died in the experiment but this does not disprove my point, nor the fact that she was not a poodle. Since the Bolshevik Revolution Russia had in any case lost all her poodles in the waves of emigration. Laika and her successful successors, Strelka and Belka, Chernuskha, and Zvyozkochaka, are by our standards, dogs of the people, very similar in their mental make-up, if not in their physical appearance, to the Barbets of the French peasant. The space dogs are the direct off-spring of those poor specimens Pavlov experimented on so successfully. Thanks to them the identity of fate between man and dog has once

A POODLE BEGINNING TO UNDERSTAND THAT PAVLOV
IS GETTING WISE TO CONDITIONED REFLEXES

more been demonstrated. Darwin told us that man and dog were built the same. Laika, blazing man's way to the moon at the price of her life, shows once more that what dog can do man will do. To quote from a learned space scientist, "Many animals, probably *including man* (my emphasis) should be able to survive the acceleration and vibration of the launching phase in a satellite or other space vehicle."

The next stage for Poodlestan under these circumstances should consist of an agonizing reappraisal. Should we be satisfied with growing affluence and what goes with it, as I have already described? Should we continue with a system of education that produces more and more poodles with less and less in their noodles, or should we go back to the rigorous discipline and challenge that made Boye, Atma, and Munito, not forgetting the glorious Moustache, such great dogs? Let us not underestimate the insidious propaganda that makes the contrary approach so attractive. Its motto is: If you can't join them, lick them. In other words a prosperous Poodlestan should attempt to make the underdeveloped parts of dogdom as prosperous, as easy-going, as consumer-conscious and credit-ridden as we are on this side of the Iron Curtain.

This is now well on its way. In an instance of the well-tried method of "finding the right type of association with the right human beings at the right time and place," Bolshoi, a white miniature, was recently sent by the British Intelligence Service to Russia under the guise of a popular subscription through a London newspaper, to seduce the

great ballerina, Ulanova. A swallow does not make the
spring and one poodle does not make Poodlestan, yet this
is surely a straw in the wind. Barely a month elapsed after
Bolshoi's arrival in the Soviet Union before he was exer-
cising full control over the entire ballet that bears his
name. Ulanova's apartment in Moscow became his private
kingdom. He had access to all the ballerina's correspond-
ence. According to Ulanova's biographer, Albert E. Kahn,
"When she went through her mail Bolshoi would seat
himself in her lap, his button eyes gleaming with delight.
'He's my rival,' I was told by Vadim Rindin (her hus-
band). 'It's a triangle. . . .' "

Bolshoi has already introduced Western habits of over-
consumption. Mr. Kahn describes his appetite as "various". "He not only consumes with dainty relish the cook-
ies, neat slices of apple, and other tidbits with which
Ulanova plied him—he also had a taste for human ap-
parel." This could easily be a crime against the state. So
we understand why Bolshoi is kept under "careful eyes"
and "his attention is diverted whenever he seems about
to satisfy his hunger for clothing". Granted that all dogs
are equal in the Soviet Union, it will obviously take time
before some poodles are more equal than others.

The challenges of space and underdevelopment are not
the only ones we have to face. Over-population can also be
a problem. I have now said enough about the dangers of
population control and the perils inherent in an unleashed
puppy-boom. The natural fears of overcrowding should
be tempered by the fact that dogdom and Poodledom do
not coincide. In other words, we can very well squeeze

out second-class, non-poodle members of dogdom and replace them, dog for dog, without pressing too hard on the available supplies. One could go further and say that in the case of a natural or man-made catastrophe in which half of dogdom would disappear, the other half would still be able to make this world a world fit for dogs to live in. The only question is to be a member of the right half.

How can we organize ourselves for this eventuality? A strong base in the richest country is a pre-requisite. This we have. A well-organized network of infiltrators closely connected with the jet set. This we are in the process of building up. Easy access to the leaders of the emerging submerged nations. This calls for a special effort.

Our long-term objective should be that not a single world leader could be photographed or televised without a poodle at his side.

In any case, better use should be made of the worldwide potential represented by the Kennel Clubs and, more specifically, the Poodle Clubs. Front organizations such as the various societies for the Prevention of Cruelty to Animals should provide a convenient façade for the unflagging pursuit of poodle supremacy.

I began my search for knowledge with a question, "Could the rising power of Poodledom be channelled into a new and glorious nation—Poodlestan?"

My quest for the past glories of Poodlestan has shown conclusively that members of our race have taken a prominent and, in more ways than one, decisive part in the progress of dogdom from the cave to the penthouse. It has also revealed many instances where apart from love secrecy was our best weapon.

In an age where the number of independent human nations can double in a decade, it is tempting to think that Poodlestan is entitled to international recognition. Surely, if a nation exists by its heart, by its past, and by a sense of its identity, apart from a certain number of inhabitants, Poodlestan is a nation. If it needs a territory on which an organized power might exercise full control, it can claim thousands of square miles in the wealthiest cities of the modern world.

Membership of Poodlestan in the United Nations would indeed impose on our breed a heavy financial burden. We can afford it. A system of taxation to finance hundreds of embassies abroad would have to be imposed. For this we may need AID. Poodlestan would have to take sides on issues dividing a badly-managed human world. As one of the smaller nations we might be called upon to provide peace-keepers at the other end of the world in uncomfortable climates. This would stir up many historical memories.

Poodlestan would indeed be one among many. Why not? But . . . perhaps *the* one among the many!

Let us stand on a united Platform irrespective of size, color or creed. Poodles of the world unite! We have nothing to lose but our leashes! Long live Poodlestan!